YOU'RE OUT OF SIGHT, CHARLIE BROWN

Books by Charles M. Schulz

Peanuts
More Peanuts
Good Grief, More Peanuts!
Good Ol' Charlie Brown
Snoopy
You're Out of Your Mind, Charlie Brown!
But We Love You, Charlie Brown
Peanuts Revisited
Go Fly a Kite, Charlie Brown
Peanuts Every Sunday
It's a Dog's Life, Charlie Brown
You Can't Win, Charlie Brown
Snoopy, Come Home
You Can Do It, Charlie Brown
We're Right Behind You, Charlie Brown
As You Like It, Charlie Brown
Sunday's Fun Day, Charlie Brown
You Need Help, Charlie Brown
Snoopy and the Red Baron
The Unsinkable Charlie Brown
You'll Flip, Charlie Brown
You're Something Else, Charlie Brown
Peanuts Treasury
You're You, Charlie Brown
You've Had It, Charlie Brown
Snoopy and His Sopwith Camel
A Boy Named Charlie Brown
You're Out of Sight, Charlie Brown

YOU'RE OUT OF SIGHT, CHARLIE BROWN

A NEW PEANUTS® BOOK

by Charles M. Schulz

HOLT, RINEHART AND WINSTON
New York • Chicago • San Francisco

Copyright © 1970 by United Feature Syndicate, Inc.
"Peanuts" comic strips copyright © 1969, 1970 by
United Feature Syndicate, Inc.

Published simultaneously in Canada by Holt, Rinehart
and Winston of Canada, Limited.

First published in book form in 1970.

First Edition

SNB: 03-085330-3

Printed in the United States of America

WHAT ARE YOU STANDING HERE FOR?

THERE'S AN OLD LEGEND THAT SAYS IF YOU STAND IN FRONT OF YOUR MAILBOX LONG ENOUGH, YOU'LL RECEIVE A VALENTINE...

SOMEBODY HAS TO MAKE UP THOSE OLD LEGENDS, DON'T THEY?

I HAVE TO WRITE A REPORT ON GEORGE WASHINGTON

I DON'T KNOW A THING ABOUT GEORGE WASHINGTON! I HATE WRITING REPORTS!

YOU CAN LOOK HIM UP IN THE ENCYCLOPEDIA..

DON'T BE RIDICULOUS! I HATE DOING THINGS LIKE THAT..

MAYBE I'LL BE LUCKY, AND THERE'LL BE SOMETHING ABOUT HIM ON TV TONIGHT

I SMELL A WET PILOT!

GRAMMA SAYS THAT NONE OF HER OTHER GRANDCHILDREN HAS A BLANKET

TELL GRAMMA THAT I'M VERY HAPPY FOR HER, AND THAT MY ADMIRATION FOR THOSE OTHER WONDERFULLY WELL-ADJUSTED GRANDCHILDREN KNOWS NO BOUNDS!

I DON'T THINK I'LL TELL HER THAT..

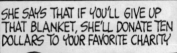

JOE SHLABOT

JOE SHLABOTNIK
FAN CLUB NEWS

VOLUME I NO. 1

DEAR FANS OF JOE SHLABOTNIK, WELL, HERE IT IS ALMOST SPRING AGAIN AND EVERYONE IS EXCITED ABOUT THE NEW BASEBALL SEASON.

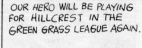

OUR HERO WILL BE PLAYING FOR HILLCREST IN THE GREEN GRASS LEAGUE AGAIN.

I REALLY SHOULD HAVE SOME PHOTOGRAPHS IN MY FAN MAGAZINE TO GIVE IT SOME CLASS, BUT I DON'T KNOW HOW TO PRINT THEM...

LAST YEAR JOE BATTED .143 AND MADE SOME SPECTACULAR CATCHES OF ROUTINE FLY BALLS. HE ALSO THREW OUT A RUNNER WHO HAD FALLEN DOWN BETWEEN FIRST AND SECOND.

WELL, FANS, THERE IT IS. REMEMBER, THIS LITTLE OL' FAN MAGAZINE IS YOURS. WE WELCOME YOUR COMMENTS.

WHO NEEDS IT?

I SHOULDN'T HAVE WELCOMED HER COMMENTS...

SCHULZ

It

It was

It was a
dark

It was a
dark and
stormy night.

GOOD WRITING IS
HARD WORK!

THAT'S A NICE BALLOON

THANK YOU..

WHAT DOES IT DO?

IT DOESN'T DO ANYTHING EXCEPT MAYBE FLY IF I LET GO OF IT..

WHY DON'T YOU PAINT THE WORD "LOVE" ON IT, AND LET IT FLY OFF SOMEPLACE?

THIS MAY CHANGE THE LIFE OF THE PERSON WHO FINDS IT...

MAYBE SOME PERSON WHO IS DEPRESSED WILL FIND IT, AND BE ENCOURAGED TO CARRY ON

MAYBE SOME GREAT LEADER WILL FIND IT, AND BE INSPIRED TO SEEK WORLD PEACE

GO, BALLOON! CARRY YOUR MESSAGE OF LOVE!

LOVE

"TO CROSS STREET PUSH BUTTON..WAIT FOR WALK SIGNAL"

YOU HAVE TO MOVE YOUR FEET, TOO!

HOW EMBARRASSING!

HERE, SNOOPY, YOU GOT A LETTER..

SHE DID IT!

SHE REPOR[T...] HEAD BEAG[LE...]

OOO₀OO₀

WHAT IS IT, SNOOPY? WHAT HAPPENED?

YOU DID IT!! YOU REPORTED SNOOPY TO THE HEAD BEAGLE!

IT WAS HIS OWN FAULT! HE NEVER WANTED TO GO RABBIT CHASING WITH ME!

SHE REPORTED ME, AND NOW I HAVE TO APPEAR BEFORE THE HEAD BEAGLE..THIS WILL BRING DISGRACE UPON THE DAISY HILL PUPPY FARM ...

IN ALL THE HISTORY OF THE DAISY HILL PUPPY FARM, NO ONE HAS EVER BEEN ORDERED TO APPEAR BEFORE THE HEAD BEAGLE !!

SCHULZ

HE'S BACK! SNOOPY'S BACK!

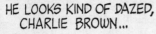

HE LOOKS KIND OF DAZED, CHARLIE BROWN...

THIS IS THE WAY YOU ALWAYS LOOK WHEN YOU RETURN FROM HAVING APPEARED BEFORE THE HEAD BEAGLE!

DID SNOOPY GET BACK?

YES, NO THANKS TO YOU! HE WAS CHARGED WITH NOT PURSUING HIS MONTHLY QUOTA OF RABBITS...

WHAT HAPPENED?

FORTUNATELY, THE HEAD BEAGLE WAS VERY UNDERSTANDING...

It was a dark and stormy night.

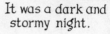

Suddenly, a shot rang out. A door slammed. The maid screamed.

Suddenly, a pirate ship appeared on the horizon!

While millions of people were starving, the king lived in luxury.

Meanwhile, on a small farm in Kansas, a boy was growing up.

Part II

IN PART TWO, I TIE ALL OF THIS TOGETHER..

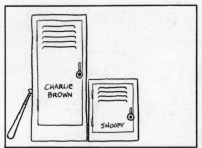

GOOD GRIEF, IT'S ALMOST NOON!

WE HAVE TO SUIT-UP FOR THE BALL GAME, SNOOPY..

HERE'S YOUR CAP...IS MINE ON RIGHT? I WANT IT STRAIGHT, BUT NOT TOO STRAIGHT...

YOURS SHOULD BE TURNED A LITTLE MORE TO THE LEFT..NOT TOO FAR BACK, EITHER, BUT NOT TOO FAR FORWARD...

WHAT DIFFERENCE DOES IT MAKE?

WHAT DIFFERENCE DOES IT MAKE? IT MAKES A LOT OF DIFFERENCE!

GIRLS JUST DON'T UNDERSTAND "SUITING-UP"!

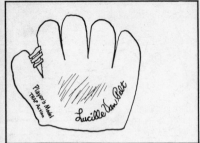

OKAY, LET'S SHOW A LITTLE LIFE OUT THERE!

HEY, MANAGER... SOME KID MUST HAVE LEFT HIS GLOVE HERE.. IT HAS HIS NAME ON IT..

SEE? RIGHT HERE... "WILLIE MAYS"... HE WROTE HIS NAME ON HIS GLOVE, SEE?

POOR KID.. HE'S PROBABLY BEEN LOOKING ALL OVER FOR IT.. WE SHOULD HAVE A "LOST AND FOUND"

I DON'T KNOW ANY KID AROUND HERE NAMED "WILLIE MAYS," DO YOU? HOW ARE WE GONNA GET IT BACK TO HIM? HE WAS PRETTY SMART PUTTING HIS NAME ON HIS GLOVE THIS WAY, THOUGH... IT'S FUNNY, I JUST DON'T REMEMBER ANY KID BY THAT NAME...

LOOK AT THE NAME ON YOUR GLOVE

WHAT?

LOOK AT YOUR OWN GLOVE... THERE'S A NAME ON IT..

"BABE RUTH"... WELL, I'LL BE! HOW IN THE WORLD DO YOU SUPPOSE I GOT HER GLOVE?!

WHAT'S THIS?

" PROPOSED NEW DOG-FEEDING SCHEDULE "

" PRE-BREAKFAST SNACK..BREAKFAST..MORNING COFFEE BREAK..PRE-NOON SNACK..LUNCH..EARLY AFTERNOON SNACK..AFTERNOON TEA..PRE-DINNER SNACK..DINNER.. TV SNACK.. BEDTIME SNACK.. AND FINALLY, A SMALL MIDNIGHT SNACK "

HMM... WELL, I'LL TELL YOU WHAT WE'LL DO... WE'LL COMPROMISE...

YOU'LL EAT ONE MEAL A DAY LIKE EVERY OTHER DOG!!!!

I HATE THOSE COMPROMISES!

SCHULZ

ONE OF US ALWAYS STAYS AWAKE IN CASE OF VAMPIRES

PSYCHIATRIC HELP 5¢

THE DOCTOR IS IN

VAMPIRES?! YOU GUYS ARE AFRAID OF VAMPIRES?

SURELY YOU MUST REALIZE THAT A FEAR OF VAMPIRES IS REALLY A PSYCHOLOGICAL PROBLEM..

FRANKLY, I DOUBT IF EITHER ONE OF YOU EVEN KNOWS WHAT A VAMPIRE LOOKS LIKE...

THE DOCTOR

It Was a
Dark and Stormy
Night
by SNOOPY

It was a dark
and stormy night

Suddenly a shot rang out.
A door slammed. The maid
screamed. Suddenly a pirate
ship appeared on the horizon.
While millions of people
were starving, the king
lived in luxury.

Meanwhile, on a small farm in
Kansas, a boy was growing up.
End of Part I

Part II
A light snow was falling, and
the little girl with the tattered shawl
had not sold a violet all day.

At that very moment, a
young intern at City Hospital
was making an important
discovery.

I MAY HAVE
WRITTEN MYSELF
INTO A CORNER...

MY MOM AND DAD WERE GOING ON A LITTLE VACATION, BUT THEY CHANGED THEIR MINDS

MOM IS KIND OF A WORRIER

SHE SAYS, WHAT IF THEY WERE DRIVING ALONG THE FREEWAY DOING ABOUT SEVENTY, AND SUDDENLY SOMETHING WENT WRONG WITH THE GLOVE COMPARTMENT?

THAT IS SOMETHING TO WORRY ABOUT

USED CAR SALE!

YES, YOU HEARD RIGHT! YOU'VE NEVER SEEN SUCH VALUES!

COME DOWN TO OUR SHOWROOM NOW!!

DON'T DELAY!! COME DOWN NOW! NOW IS THE TIME! NOW! NOW! NOW!

HELP!

WELL! DID THAT NASTY OL' POP FLY AWAKEN YOU? DID IT DISTURB YOUR BEAUTY SLEEP?

I'M SORRY IF THE SOUND OF FLY BALLS LANDING BEHIND YOU IS DEPRIVING YOU OF YOUR REST!

PERHAPS WE SHOULD SOFTEN THE INFIELD SO THE BALL WON'T MAKE SO MUCH NOISE WHEN IT LANDS BEHIND YOU...

WAAH!

OH, GOOD GRIEF! NOW, I'VE HURT HIS FEELINGS...

I'M SORRY, SNOOPY.. I APOLOGIZE.. I SHOULDN'T HAVE BEEN SO SARCASTIC.. I GUESS I DON'T KNOW HOW TO HANDLE PLAYERS...I'M A TERRIBLE MANAGER... I APOLOGIZE..

IT'S GOOD TO BE BACK WITH MY OLD OUTFIT!

WELL, HOW WAS YOUR VACATION, CHARLIE BROWN?

VACATIONS ARE DREADED, SUFFERED, ENDURED, TOLERATED, SPOILED, RUINED AND WASTED...

VACATIONS CAN BE GREAT, TERRIBLE, WONDERFUL, AWFUL, DELIGHTFUL AND STUPID

I SPENT MY WHOLE VACATION WORRYING ABOUT MY DOG..

YOU NEED A VACATION, CHARLIE BROWN!

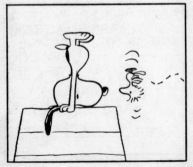

I'M HUNGRY

MY HEAD WAS SOUND ASLEEP, BUT MY STOMACH WAS WIDE AWAKE...

IT'S MIDNIGHT, AND I'M STARVING TO DEATH, AND THERE'S NO WAY FOR ME TO GET A LITTLE SNACK

IF I WERE A STUPID CAT, I COULD GO OUT AND CATCH A MOUSE

MY STOMACH NEEDS A SLEEPING PILL...NO, MY HEAD NEEDS A SLEEPING PILL AND MY STOMACH NEEDS A SNACK...

NOW, HOW IN THE WORLD DID HE KNOW I WAS HUNGRY?

WHO CAN SLEEP WITH ALL THAT MUMBLING GOING ON?

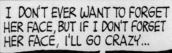

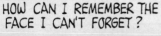
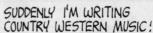

I'VE FINISHED THE DRAWING FOR THE COVER OF YOUR NEW NOVEL...

SEE? IT SHOWS A BUNCH OF PIRATES AND FOREIGN LEGIONNAIRES FIGHTING SOME COWBOYS, AND SOME LIONS AND TIGERS AND ELEPHANTS LEAPING THROUGH THE AIR TOWARD A GIRL WHO IS TIED TO A SUBMARINE

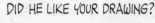

DID HE LIKE YOUR DRAWING?

IT NEEDS MORE TIGERS!

It was a dark and stormy night. Suddenly, a shot rang out!

The maid screamed. A door slammed.

Suddenly, a pirate ship appeared on the horizon!

THIS TWIST IN THE PLOT WILL BAFFLE MY READERS...

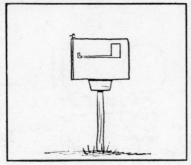

OH, EXCUSE ME..

THAT'S ALL RIGHT... I'M EXPECTING WORD FROM MY PUBLISHER...

HEY, SNOOPY, LOOK!

IT'S A LETTER FROM YOUR PUBLISHER..

REALLY?

I'M AFRAID TO OPEN IT....

BE CAREFUL WHEN YOU DO...THERE'S PROBABLY A CHECK INSIDE!

TELL ME THAT YOU LOVE ME, KISS ME ON THE NOSE AND GIVE ME A BIG HUG!

LOOK OUT, EVERYBODY! I'M GONNA BE CRABBY FOR THE REST OF THE DAY!!

HERE, SNOOPY, THIS IS FOR YOU..

OH, NO!

I KNOW WHAT IT IS WITHOUT EVEN LOOKING!

I HATE THIS TIME OF YEAR!

THIS IS WHEN YOU HAVE TO FILL OUT A REPORT TO THE HEAD BEAGLE ON WHAT YOU'VE DONE ALL YEAR..

1. How many rabbits have you chased?
"NONE". HOW EMBARRASSING...
2. How many cats have you chased?
"NONE". THAT'S A GOOD WAY TO GET RACKED UP!

3. How many owls did you howl at?
"TWELVE, BUT I SAW ONLY TWO"...STUPID OWLS!
4. Did you take part in any Fox Hunts?
"NO"... I HAVE NO DESIRE TO BE STOMPED ON BY A CLUMSY HORSE!

THIS IS THE PART I HATE...
5. Relationships with humans....
   a. How did you treat your master?
   b. Were you friendly with neighborhood children?
   c. Did you bite anyone?
THESE ARE VERY PERSONAL QUESTIONS...

Return the yellow form to the Head Beagle with your dues, and keep the blue form for your files..Report must be postmarked no later than Jan. 15th

WHAT A NUISANCE..

I'D REALLY LIKE TO JUST FORGET THE WHOLE THING..

U.S. MAIL

EXCEPT THAT SOMEDAY I MAY GET TO BE THE HEAD BEAGLE!

SCHULZ

IT'S RAINING OUTSIDE.. I LOVE RAINY DAYS...

SOMEDAY, WHEN WE'RE MARRIED, AND IT'S A RAINY DAY, I'LL MAKE A FIRE IN THE FIREPLACE, AND WHILE YOU'RE PRACTICING THE PIANO, I'LL BRING US SOME TEA AND TOAST

NO WAY

I HATE RAINY DAYS!

WHY DOES IT ALWAYS RAIN WHEN I WANT TO DO SOMETHING?

ACTUALLY, IT DOESN'T REALLY... IT ONLY SEEMS THAT IT DOES BECAUSE YOU'RE UPSET RIGHT NOW, AND YOU'VE FORGOTTEN ABOUT THE MANY SUNNY DAYS WE'VE HAD WHEN..

WHY DOES IT **ALWAYS** RAIN WHEN I WANT TO DO SOMETHING?

YOU'RE A VERY UNLUCKY PERSON..

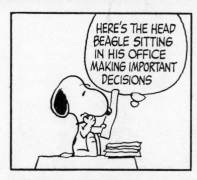

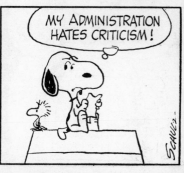

THE HEAD BEAGLE HAS DISAPPEARED!

SNIF

HE'S GONE! THE HEAD BEAGLE HAS DISAPPEARED!!

I'LL BET THE PRESSURE GOT TO BE TOO MUCH FOR HIM...

BUT WHERE COULD HE HAVE GONE?

HELLO?

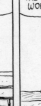
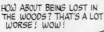

HEY, BIG BROTHER, WAKE UP!

WHAT'S THE MATTER?

I WANT TO ASK YOU ABOUT SCHOOL...IF YOU'RE LATE FOR THE FIRST DAY OF SCHOOL, WILL THEY KILL YOU?

GOOD GRIEF, NO! WHERE DID YOU GET THAT IDEA?

WELL, WHAT IF YOU DON'T KNOW WHERE TO GO, OR YOU FORGET YOUR LUNCH, OR GET LOST IN THE HALLWAY? WHAT IF YOU CAN'T REMEMBER YOUR LOCKER COMBINATION?

ARE YOU SUPPOSED TO BRING A LOOSE-LEAF BINDER? HOW WIDE? TWO HOLES OR THREE? DO BIG KIDS BEAT YOU UP ON THE PLAYGROUND? DO THEY TRIP YOU AND KNOCK YOU DOWN?

LOOK, JUST STOP WORRYING.. EVERYTHING WILL BE ALL RIGHT..GO BACK TO BED..

WHAT IF I CAN'T REMEMBER MY LOCKER COMBINATION?

SCHULZ

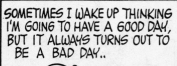

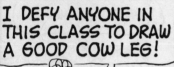

MISS SWANSON, I DON'T UNDERSTAND THE FOURTH PROBLEM

OF COURSE, I DON'T REALLY UNDERSTAND THE OTHER THREE PROBLEMS, EITHER...

ACTUALLY, I DON'T UNDERSTAND MATH AT ALL

LET'S FACE IT... I DON'T EVEN UNDERSTAND SCHOOL!

BOY, DID YOU EVER GOOF ME UP!

YOU HAD ME TAKE MY LUNCH TO SCHOOL IN A LUNCH BOX...DO YOU KNOW WHAT HAPPENED?

ALL THE OTHER KIDS WERE BROWN-BAGGING IT!! I FELT LIKE A FOOL!

YOU GAVE ME BAD ADVICE, BIG BROTHER!

I CAN'T STAND ALL THIS RESPONSIBILITY..

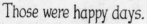

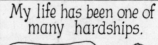

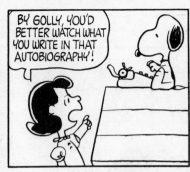

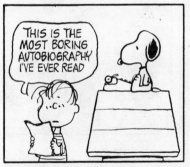

BOOT!

I LOST YOUR FOOTBALL, BIG BROTHER...I KICKED IT SO HIGH IT NEVER CAME DOWN..

DON'T WORRY ABOUT IT... IT'LL COME DOWN...

BIG BROTHERS KNOW EVERYTHING!

NUMBERS ARE BEAUTIFUL..

I LIKE TWOS THE BEST...THEY'RE SORT OF GENTLE..THREES AND FIVES ARE MEAN, BUT A FOUR IS ALWAYS PLEASANT.. I LIKE SEVENS AND EIGHTS, TOO, BUT NINES ALWAYS SCARE ME... TENS ARE GREAT...

HAVE YOU DONE THOSE DIVISION PROBLEMS FOR TOMORROW?

NOTHING SPOILS NUMBERS FASTER THAN A LOT OF ARITHMETIC!

I LEARNED SOMETHING IN SCHOOL TODAY

I SIGNED UP FOR FOLK GUITAR, COMPUTER PROGRAMMING, STAINED GLASS ART, SHOEMAKING AND A NATURAL FOODS WORKSHOP..

I GOT SPELLING, HISTORY, ARITHMETIC AND TWO STUDY PERIODS

SO WHAT DID YOU LEARN?

I LEARNED THAT WHAT YOU SIGN UP FOR AND WHAT YOU GET ARE TWO DIFFERENT THINGS

I'M SORRY, SNOOPY.. A LEAF FELL ON YOUR DINNER...

RATS! I THOUGHT MAYBE I WAS GETTING A SALAD!

THIS IS GOING TO BE A DUMB DAY..

THIS IS GOING TO BE ONE OF THOSE DUMB DAYS WHEN I SAY DUMB THINGS, AND DO DUMB THINGS AND EVERYONE TELLS ME I'M DUMB!

MAYBE YOU SHOULD GO BACK HOME, AND GO TO BED...

I NEVER DO ANYTHING THAT SMART ON A DUMB DAY...

TRICK OR TREAT

SMAK

THAT'S THE BEST TREAT YOU'LL GET ALL NIGHT, SWEETIE!

HOW DO YOU TELL A PUMPKIN THAT YOU DON'T NEED HIM ANY MORE?

GO! GO! GO!

FANTASTIC!

CHARLIE BROWN, I JUST SAW THE MOST UNBELIEVABLE FOOTBALL GAME EVER PLAYED...

WHAT A COMEBACK!

THE HOME TEAM WAS BEHIND SIX-TO-NOTHING WITH ONLY THREE SECONDS TO PLAY..THEY HAD THE BALL ON THEIR OWN ONE-YARD LINE...

THE QUARTERBACK TOOK THE BALL, FADED BACK BEHIND HIS OWN GOAL POSTS AND THREW A PERFECT PASS TO THE LEFT END, WHO WHIRLED AWAY FROM FOUR GUYS AND RAN ALL THE WAY FOR A TOUCHDOWN! THE FANS WENT WILD! YOU SHOULD HAVE SEEN THEM!

PEOPLE WERE JUMPING UP AND DOWN, AND WHEN THEY KICKED THE EXTRA POINT, THOUSANDS OF PEOPLE RAN OUT ONTO THE FIELD LAUGHING AND SCREAMING! THE FANS AND THE PLAYERS WERE SO HAPPY THEY WERE ROLLING ON THE GROUND AND HUGGING EACH OTHER AND DANCING AND EVERYTHING!

IT WAS FANTASTIC!

HOW DID THE OTHER TEAM FEEL?

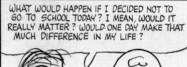

SHOVEL YOUR WALK FOR A QUARTER?

WHAT IF IT SNOWS TOMORROW, AND COVERS UP OUR WALK AGAIN? DO WE GET OUR QUARTER BACK?

NO, BY THEN I WILL HAVE SPENT IT IN RIOTOUS LIVING...

FORGET IT!

HERE'S THE WORLD-FAMOUS HOCKEY PLAYER TAPING HIS STICK BEFORE THE GAME..

WE HOCKEY PLAYERS ARE VERY FUSSY ABOUT THE WAY WE TAPE OUR STICKS

SOMETIMES, OF COURSE, WE HAVE A LITTLE TROUBLE WITH THE TAPE...